Hugs FOR Caregivers

Hugs for Caregivers

Pauline J. Sheehan

To the Kecks

Pauline Sheehan

WINEPRESS WP PUBLISHING

Packaged by WinePress Publishing, PO Box 1406, Mukilteo, WA 98275. The views expressed or implied in this work do not necessarily reflect those of WinePress Publishing. Ultimate design, content, and editorial accuracy of this work is the responsibility of the author.

ISBN 1-57921-105-4
Library of Congress Catalog Card Number: 98-60294

Endorsements

"I want this book. It is wonderful, warm and fun."

—Sharon Harms, author

"Just like a real support group these caregivers on a retreat find humor, support, and practical advice from each other. All this — from a small book — is for the caregiver reader who can't get away."

—Treasure Omdahl, Bereavement Services Coordinator
Hospice and Home Care

"Pauline Sheehan is certainly qualified to write this book. She has a clear and specific vision."

—Kimn Swenson Gollnick, inspirational writer

"Pauline states that caregiving is love in action. She has put her 'love in action' in *Hugs for Caregivers*. From the beginning right on through the appendix, this book is a wonderful gift. The suggestions in the appendix are especially helpful for anyone wanting to provide care and encouragement to caregivers."

—Nancy Slind, Care Team Coordinator

"Interesting format. New concept. Caregivers can pick up and read short sections."

—Sharon Stanley, RN Certified Geriatric Nurse
Alzheimer Unit Coordinator

"Pauline uniquely acknowledges those 'hugs' which support through the challenging caregiver times. She gives us an opportunity to feel, think, listen, and enjoy the relationship. Enjoy *Hugs for Caregivers*. I did."

—Joanne Ozaki-Moore RN, M.Ed.
Director, Professional Services for Hospice and Home Care

"The message is that caregiving is costing you something whether you realize it or not. *Hugs for Caregivers* helps you know it is justifiable to replenish yourself."

—Linda Wagner, Caregiver

"You have a keen sense of humor and love a good time."

—from a fortune cookie

"Knowing where the caregivers are coming from, they have lots of good advice."

—Marcel Elfers, Physical Therapist
Home Care

"I like the format of the people conversing."

—Patricia Kimes LPN, Nursing Home Activity Director

Table of Contents

Embrace Your Emotions

Embrace Your Spirit

Embrace Your Sense of Humor

Welcome

 Welcome

Hugs for Caregivers is a gift book for you the caregiver, which was conceived out of my respect for caregivers. I faced caregiving issues with my children, sister, and father; and relied on my husband as my caregiver during a four-year illness. Throughout my work in coronary critical care, nursing home administration, cardiac rehab, home care case management, and diabetes education, I saw caregivers being catapulted in to their responsibilities. Their courage, stamina, and determination was similar to our country's early pioneers who courageously forged ahead into unknown territory.

Even though your body is wondrously made, your own physical needs are important: as the airline stewardess cautions, "Secure your own oxygen mask before assisting others."

Although your spirit is indomitable, you deserve an embrace during this time of caregiving. Your first hug, a squeeze through the birth canal, brought you life. Your survival continues to depend on hugs—being embraced, loved, and encouraged.

I envisioned a book that would embrace caregivers. As the author, I created caregivers from my imagination, assigned them topics, chose a script format, and allowed them to speak from their hearts. This brings up the discussion of whether it is true. Yes, their experiences will stand the test of truth because you will see yourself in their conversations.

If I were going to imagine a caregivers respite, I would arrange a summer retreat high in the mountains, sequestered within the massive arms of a summer lodge. Colorful, cushioned patio chairs would entice them to relax on the deck, watch the sun rise across alpine gardens, and smell the early dawn's fragrance wafting through the air. Here, they would be safe to share their hopes, yearnings, and joys; and reveal their indomitable human spirits. *Hugs for Caregivers* welcomes you to join them on their reprieve from fatigue, loneliness and grief. Listen in on their conversations, for they not only give you permission to take care of yourself, they tell you how to do it.

The first to arrive is a lady with a clip to her step. "Good morning. My name is Andrea Gordan. My daughter is four and my son is ten. I'm here because I took a leave of absence from work and office politics when we moved Granny to our acreage."

A lithe, weathered man in western boots steps on to the deck and tips his cowboy hat. "I'm Rodney Windmere, call me Rex. I'm here because The Missus and I—as we call it—are slowing down. We hitched up fifty-two years ago and raised all of our children on the farm. All seven of them—children, that is—not farms."

"I'm Lucia Rodriguez. I'm here because my husband was disabled from a car accident. We have three teenage sons." She sighs as she drops into a chair.

An energetic young man strides toward us. His confidence hints at wisdom beyond his years. "Beautiful morning. My name is Kahn Sato. I'm here because my wife's on chemotherapy. I'm a building contractor. Our children are ages three, five, and seven."

A sprightly woman's eyes sparkle in contrast to the frailty of her body. Flashing a mischievous smile, she fluffs a pillow. "I'm Rachel Goldstein. Most people call me Mrs. Goldstein. Papa got ill very suddenly. I'm new to being a caregiver. Now, don't you worry about me. I'm doing fine . . . as long as my back holds out." With that breathy announcement, she throws her pillow on her chair and sits down.

A lanky boy, wearing a baseball hat, bounds up the path. "Hi, I'm Scott Nathan. I go by Scott." He eyes the deck floor that is planked wood. "I left my skateboard in the car. It looks like I'm the only teenager here. I'm spending the summer with Grandpops. He's really my great grandpa." He finds the nearest chair. The women give him motherly looks and the men nod their camaraderie.

With this introduction, the caregivers welcome you to join them on their retreat, titled *Hugs for Caregivers*.

REX: Should I speak first? Wow, what a beautiful place. I could settle on this deck for the entire summer. But, down to bedrock. How do we get started?

KAHN: We could start at the beginning.

REX: Ok, what do you think of the cover?

KAHN: The umbrella is interesting. A reprieve. A protection. A shelter. A place to sequester. It reminds me of philosopher Samuel Johnson's 1755 quote, "There was a time a man might Sequester himself to review his life and purify his heart."

REX: The two gals look secure under it. They look happy, too.

LUCIA: Actually, they are giggling.

KAHN: I wonder what they are up to?

ANDREA: They are probably caregivers, delighted to get a reprieve from their responsibilities. Let's get on to the topics. What is first?

Embrace
Your *Body*

 Sing

ANDREA: Sing. This is a fresh, new day, which makes it a good time to talk about singing. I sing in the shower, and I sing in the car, and I sing in the garden. Anywhere my spirit wants to sing, yet where no one can hear me.

KAHN: What do you sing?

ANDREA: A Pavarotti rendition.

KAHN: May I ask which song from his repertoire?

ANDREA: "The Old Gray Mare, She Ain't What She Used to Be."

KAHN: Pavarotti sings that?

ANDREA: Maybe when he's tired.

KAHN: I don't think so.

ANDREA: When I'm tired, I sing it. Pavarotti would be proud of me. Of course, he would have to pay admission . . . to my shower, my car, or my garden.

KAHN: You jest!

ANDREA: That's allowed. Joking is allowed, and so is singing. If Cervantes can say, "He who sings scares away his woes," then I can sing in the shower.

MRS. GOLDSTEIN: On to my singing story. In Tel Aviv, the birds sing on the back streets where the garbage waits in the heat. I heard them before I spotted them. Not a few little chirps early in the morning, but singing, happy singing, all day long.

KAHN: What repertoire did they sing?

MRS. GOLDSTEIN: Shalom. To me, they were singing in spite of their surroundings.

REX: You're so poetic. Have you heard the bob-o-links high in the Cascades? High-pitched, melodic chirps. bob-o-link, bob-o-link, bob-o-link. They must be sopranos. On our camp-outs, from inside my sleeping bag, I listen to bob-o-links chirping and coffee percolating . . . especially if the grandchildren put the coffee on. It warms my heart.

ANDREA: You're not talking about singing, you're talking about someone waiting on you.

REX: Yep. That is my favorite subject.

ANDREA: But we were talking about singing.

REX: And the next topic?

ANDREA: Energize.

 # Energize

MRS. GOLDSTEIN: What I want to know about energy is where to get it.

ANDREA: That's a good question. Exercise is what helped me. I would come home from work exhausted and drag myself to aerobics at the gym. But I returned home rejuvenated. The more faithfully I exercised, the more energy I had. Now that I'm on leave, I'm more tired. I didn't think about it, but I stopped my aerobics class. Maybe I'll start going again or put on the Phase III, advanced aerobic dancing.

LUCIA: Brag, brag.

ANDREA: Ok. The honest answer. I do every fourth count.

LUCIA: Whew. That makes me feel better.

MRS. GOLDSTEIN: I might try exercise classes for senior citizens when I get the energy to sign the application. Seriously, I know that exercise gives energy, but how do I get started?

ANDREA: Start simply. Stretch. Cats make it look like it feels good.

MRS. GOLDSTEIN: Oh, I already do that. Good for me, I'm doing something right. My morning stretch limbers me up. It is more important now that I do more lifting . . . and pulling, and scooting, and turning. My whole body feels better. The first thing in the morning, I put coffee on. Then stretch. I reach as far up as I can with one arm, then the other. I put my hand on my hips and lean back to stretch my lower back and my back holds out longer on the days that I remember to do my stretches. When the coffee is done, I quit stretching. Talking about coffee. Are there refreshments around here?

KAHN: Sure. Whatever you bring, we will share with you. Ha!

SCOTT: I could use a Pepsi.

ANDREA: Until refreshments magically appear, we can talk about other stretches. I do pushups against a wall, keeping my heels on the floor and stretching my calves and Achilles tendon. This is good to do before taking a walk.

KAHN: Fabulous. To think that it isn't taxed.

MRS. GOLDSTEIN: What kind of exercise do the rest of you do?

SCOTT: I skateboard and shoot baskets.

KAHN: I have a stationary bike, which I don't use. I know why there are so many used ones for sale. The seats are hard.

ANDREA: Try folding up a bathroom rug to put over the seat. I should put the bathroom rug over the scale. Just as I think how much I would enjoy a walk in the fresh air, it rains. I don't want the air that fresh.

KAHN: Freshly washed.

LUCIA: Fresh air gives me a fresh attitude. I line-dance to the TV dancers. Of course, that is if no one is looking. If I was dancing with them live, I'd have flubbed them all up.

ANDREA: It sounds like fun. Do you wear cowboy boots? Or are you a line-dancer in tennis shoes?

LUCIA: [Blush] Would you believe house slippers?

SCOTT: I rap. I don't dance with girls.

MRS. GOLDSTEIN: My dance experience is unique, but for me . . . it's fun. I play "Ring Around the Rosy" with my grandchild. He is only two, so we whirl until he is dizzy.

LUCIA: That's where I'll be if I really do try that line dancing. Of course, I might be better off if I didn't dance in my house slippers.

MRS. GOLDSTEIN: Good for you; you keep a routine.

ANDREA: My husband takes walks when we travel. We have been to some interesting places, like down Pennsylvania Avenue in Washington, DC. We walked the first four blocks of the Iditarod race, but it was in September when the temperature was 42 degrees. There wasn't a dogsled in sight—nor snow either. Where have the rest of you been?

MRS. GOLDSTEIN: We walked on the Tel Aviv beach promenade. That was beautiful at sunset. It reflected across the Mediterranean.

KAHN: We walked the beach by Kennebunkport. I remember crawling over the debris-covered rocks after a storm. We were reminded that we, like the rocks, would survive the storm. When my wife started chemo, we talked about that walk.

REX: Now, The Missus and I don't get as far. We walk along the irrigation ditches in Treasure Valley. In the summer, you can smell alfalfa. It smells green.

KAHN: Green is a smell?

REX: Yep. That's alfalfa. Once you smelled it, you would know.

 Eat

LUCIA: Eating should be fun.

MRS. GOLDSTEIN: Here is how I make it fun: I set up three TV tray tables in the bedroom so that Papa doesn't have to walk as far. I set the table with china, silverware, and bright napkins. The third is for the food and a centerpiece. In the summer, I arrange fresh flowers. Sometimes I display pictures of the grandchildren. On our anniversary, I brought out our wedding portrait. I don't use lace and linen and candles like I used to; I go for bright and washable.

SCOTT: I'm working up an appetite.

LUCIA: I'm the opposite. I get busy and forget to eat.

REX: By the time I cook what The Missus can eat, I am done cooking. I forget about myself. Eating is part of taking care of myself. The busier that I am, the more important food is.

ANDREA: I munch all day. It figures! I should be eating nourishing foods, and, in my case, correct portions.

SCOTT: Like racecars that require high-performance fuels.

LUCIA: You're right. We also benefit from high-quality fuel. The more strenuous or stressful our work, the higher our nutrition requirements are. Good nutrition comes from common sense eating, it is not complicated or expensive. How do we plan our food? Let me guess. It's in the food pyramid that is printed on cracker boxes and bread wrappers. Six to eleven servings from the bread, cereal, pasta, or rice category every day. Three servings at each meal is easier to understand.

ANDREA: And candy bars?

LUCIA: None.

ANDREA: Oh, yes. It's in the chocolate section.

LUCIA: There is no chocolate section, but there is a fat section. Up there with the sugar group.

ANDREA: Wouldn't you know! It's the little section at the tippy-top, but it is in the pyramid.

KAHN: I make my kids eat their fruits and vegetables, because it's the right thing for a parent to do. How many servings am I supposed to make them eat?

LUCIA: It's on the box. Three to five servings of vegetables. Round that off to one per meal. Two to four servings of fruit means one serving at each meal. There you are, Kahn. To make it simple, eat some fruits or vegetables at each meal. Eat three servings a day of meat, eggs or nuts, and also three servings of milk or cheese.

Choose something from each group for each meal. That balance gives you the right combination of . . . as Scott says . . . fuel. Obviously, this food plan doesn't include skipping meals, or, in my case, skipping several meals. Back to the basics. A car that runs out of fuel is going to end up at the side of the road. I don't want to run out of energy. I need all of the energy that I can get to keep up with my teenagers and to take care of my husband. I need high octane. To think that a balance of all of the food groups is the secret!

KAHN: What are those groups again? Take it from the top.

LUCIA: No, from the bottom. The bottom is the healthiest. Starches (breads, cereals, rice, pasta) is on the bottom. Vegetables and fruits are next. Meats and milk is next. And fat and sugar is on the tippy-top, which means teeny tiny amounts.

ANDREA: Don't knock the top; that's where the chocolate is.

LUCIA: A good breakfast starts the day off—advice I could use for myself. What are some ideas for healthy snacks?

KAHN: My wife's sister solved that for us. She keeps dried fruit and nuts in bowls. "Concentrated nutrients," she says. She also keeps the nonfat yogurt in the fridge. My wife has never kept junk food, like potato chips, pop, and bakery goodies in the house, so we aren't used to eating them.

REX: What I do is boil up cabbage and onions and carrots. Then freeze it. When I'm ready to use it, I can add beef, or chicken, or tomato, or potatoes, or whatever.

LUCIA: Those are good ideas. On our way to health and energy!

KAHN: Keeps us perking.

SCOTT: Revs us up.

Embrace Your *Family*

 Love

ANDREA: Do you see what I see, Scott? Refreshments are coming. There's a Pepsi on ice. Just in time, the sun is high and warm. As we grab a drink, we can talk about love. That's what caregiving is: love in action. I think each of us is already showing love.

MRS. GOLDSTEIN: Papa knows I love him. That's why I'm his nurse from sunrise to sunset—and all night, too. I love him in practical ways, such as giving him meals, and clean clothes, and fresh bedding.

LUCIA: The advantage of saying the words, "I love you," is to hear it echoed back to you. There is a spirit of love in our home, because we sprinkle the air with the words, "thank you," "please," "excuse me" and pleasantries like winks, hugs, kisses and smiles . . . and pats.

ANDREA: I give Granny a peck on her cheek and say, "Love ya." She mouths back, "I love you," and flashes her lopsided grin. Warms my heart. Like Lucia says, if you sprinkle the air with love, it reciprocates.

SCOTT: Grandpops goes to bed early. He gives me a kiss and says he loves me. It's kind of embarrassing . . . yet I like it. Maybe I'll say, "I love you, too."

MRS. GOLDSTEIN: Here is my idea. A cheerful-looking house brings life and love to a home. Balloons are colorful and don't take up much space. Posters, photos, oil paintings, sculptures, toss pillows, flowers . . .

LUCIA: Music. Any kind. Harp, guitar, accordion, violin, or vocals. We collect folk music from Spanish Tango to Western hoedown, from German accordion to Southern gospel.

KAHN: How about Riverdance?

LUCIA: I would like to buy it. The Riverdancers could come to our house for a live performance and it wouldn't be any noisier than it already is.

MRS. GOLDSTEIN: Or a quiet celebration like crooning with papa to an old Frank Sinatra record.

LUCIA: My teenagers choose their own music when they help me with their father's physical therapy. I would think it would drive him crazy, but he enjoys it. Having two help really makes a difference.

REX: Our grandchildren come over on the weekends. I like to have them around. They are useful, too. They hoe the garden for the week—their dad put them up to it. My son calls from work and asks if he can pick up anything on his way home. It saves a couple of dollars to not have the pharmacy mail the prescriptions.

MRS. GOLDSTEIN: I probably should delegate more than I do. But I have a system; I know what Papa wants and no one else can do it like it should be done.

Rex: What about your back? You said it was giving out.

Mrs. Goldstein: I'm trying to grin and bear it . . . except the grin part, I'm not so good at.

Kahn: My wife seems relieved that I ask for help. I think that while I was worrying about her, she was worrying about me. Delegating is a loving thing to do. Mrs. Goldstein, I think that your husband wants your health preserved. So when do you start delegating?

Mrs. Goldstein: You're asking hard questions. Not now . . . at least I hope that I will never have to.

Kahn: What are your criteria for when to ask for help?

Mrs. Goldstein: Oh, I am to start thinking about the criteria even though I may never have to use it.

Kahn: Yes, if the situation occurs that you need more help, you will recognize it?

Mrs. Goldstein: That's right. Your wife's sister comes. How did you decide?

Kahn: We listed the facts. During chemotherapy, my wife can't take care of the kids, or do housework. Her sister has a family of her own, so she comes over intermittently. We know when the chemo will be, so we plan for it.

Mrs. Goldstein: What if you need more help, later on?

KAHN: I'm like you. I don't want that time to come, although I am keeping track of the offers and writing it in a notebook.

MRS. GOLDSTEIN: So you think that I should set my criteria ahead of time?

KAHN: Yes.

MRS. GOLDSTEIN: Any other ideas?

LUCIA: Heal old wounds.

KAHN: That's a sensitive issue. I see the value of living at peace with my family, especially when illness has brought us to a crisis. Our emotions are honed down to where they are raw. Lucia calls it "sprinkle the air with love." I call it "keep your feet on the ground." For me, it is heal old wounds with my brother-in-law. Now, I need his help and am hesitant to ask. I haven't resolved that.

MRS. GOLDSTEIN: What's a good way to start?

KAHN: A safe way. Start by not aggravating the situation, which is all I can do right now.

 Remember

REX: I tell stories. My grandchildren hang on me . . . waiting for the punch line. Of course, I drawl it out to tease them. I tell them that O'Henry says, "Life is made of sobs, sniffles, and smiles." When we were young, my papa told stories of the floods that destroyed acres of his ranch. They were pioneers. They didn't rely on technical forecasting; they relied on their neighbors.

MRS. GOLDSTEIN: We are mentors for our grandchildren. Hopefully, we can pass on our values that way. One way to remember the good times is by journaling. I started it to help me remember some of the grandchildren's antics. My granddaughter phoned to tell me she couldn't come to visit. She said, "I have a dentist disappointment." I had to write that one down.

ANDREA: I could ask my sisters to help Granny with a scrapbook for the pictures that are at their homes. We would all treasure the memories. The assortment of papers and templates, pens and fancy-bladed scissors, stickers and logos make it a craft instead of work.

SCOTT: Grandpops has a cardboard box of stuff. Old letters, clippings, photos, military memorabilia, and old coins, too. A gold mine! He could tell me about it, and I could organize it and label it and write what he said. We'll do it in the mornings; he's more alert then.

MRS. GOLDSTEIN: And when you go home at the end of the summer, your mother would be interested in her father's stories.

SCOTT: Surprised, too! She doesn't think I listen to adults.

REX: On my birthday, my sons sat me and my brother down in front of the video and asked us questions. At first, we were self-conscious, but then we started hamming it up. Got me to thinking about the kites we made as kids. I told about flying kites, how we made them, and how far they would go, and how disappointed we were when the string broke. It wasn't the complex plot kind of story. We shaved off splinters from the rafters in the attic for the struts, and waxed bread wrappers were the paper. They did fly!

# Communicate

ANDREA: My four-year-old comes home from preschool and sits on Granny's bed and chatters and chatters. Granny listens much more patiently than I do.

LUCIA: I have a neighbor who lets me talk out my feelings. She doesn't live in my house, and she's not a relative, so she has a unique perspective. And I can trust her not to tell.

MRS. GOLDSTEIN: Papa listens to me even if I grumble. I know he doesn't feel good himself, but he lets me confide in him.

SCOTT: Grandpops is a good listener. In the evening—if he hasn't fallen asleep in his chair we talk. Mostly, he nods and listens. Once in a while he says, "Hum."

KAHN: We know we need to talk in order to stay on the same wavelength, or my favorite expression "keep our feet on the ground." I'm challenged to focus on how to do it better.

ANDREA: This quote is by Robert Anderson, Ed.D.: "Make sure you listen. No matter what it takes; perhaps setting a timer. Listen to each other. In real close relationships, there is such an emotional component."

Let me try to paraphrase it. When we are in an intense situation—like all of us are—we need to really hear what each other is saying.

Since Granny came to stay with us, my husband and I haven't had as much time to be with each other. We used to talk after supper while the oldest kids cleared the table, but now I get up too fast in order to catch up with my chores.

REX: The Missus and I are readers. She reads her books and I read mine, so we have lots to talk about. I read Westerns, historical fiction, horticulture, and architecture. I like books about Alaska, gold mining, glacier formation . . . those kinds of things. The Missus reads historical novels in European settings.

KAHN: How does that apply to communication?

REX: Fiction is true, just like real life . . . It tells us lots about life. The stories set the stage to talk about serious things in our lives, and help us make decisions.

SCOTT: E-mail works. Grandpops doesn't have a computer, but his neighbor does. I e-mail my folks about how he is doing, how his doctor appointments went.

REX: I don't have the newfangled electronic gadgets, but I have cassettes . . . because I like the music.

SCOTT: You could record on them and mail them out. Cassettes are letters with sound effects.

KAHN: Cassettes don't have to be recorded all at once. I could record little snatches perhaps at meals. A round-robin cassette! Send it around until it returns. My wife could put in a greeting and my preschooler could sing the new song she learned, or my second grader could toot a little on his play trumpet. Actually, he is obnoxious on it, but it would be cute for those who haven't heard it.

REX: If they want the full affect, they could rewind and play it back.

KAHN: I doubt if they would want to.

MRS. GOLDSTEIN: My bird could chatter something. He's not embarrassed at all about what he says.

REX: What does your bird say?

MRS. GOLDSTEIN: That is off the subject.

REX: Then put me on your round-robin.

MRS. GOLDSTEIN: You're not a relative. You're a caregiver.

REX: [Sigh] I think I am losing out on the juicy talk from the bird.

SCOTT: Don't forget videos—cassettes with a view.

KAHN: Letters with sound effects and a visual punch. Actually, this sounds easier than letters or cassettes. We've had our video camera for several years. I photograph postcards and snapshots of our vacations. I added on the birthday parties . . . and school performances.

MRS. GOLDSTEIN: I put together a video. I combined old photos of Papa with more recent ones. Then I videoed him telling stories about the photos. We sent out copies to my brothers and sisters. Papa was able to watch our granddaughter's graduation by video. You can copy old slides and old home movies. If you wanted to get fancy, you could add music. You could video your garden as it grows. Or get a photo of the new horse—if you have a horse.

SCOTT: How do you fill up two hours?

MRS. GOLDSTEIN: We didn't.

KAHN: If you send, you get.

Embrace
Your *Friends*

 # Pop Popcorn

SCOTT: Yahoo! Lunch is here. I'm ready to chow down.

ANDREA: Should we talk about popcorn while we eat our lunch? What about popcorn? It is easy and cheap. Lucia, our local nutritionist, will be impressed because it is low in calories, high in fiber, and is a complex carbohydrate. I know ways of fixing that. Caramelizing it. I am versatile with adding calories and not limited to chocolate as my only gastronomical weakness.

KAHN: Popcorn is social. It makes me think of going to the movies or renting a video and inviting friends over. And I don't have to dress up.

REX: Yep. The Missus and I love company. Refreshments are a challenge. If I sent out invitations, they would say RDOH: Refreshments Don't Originate Here. I think the popcorn would solve that, except, I'm the housekeeper now, and I'm not as good at it as The Missus.

LUCIA: Herds of teens come through our house. They travel in packs, you know. I learned some shortcuts. Shine up the kitchen and the bathroom, pick up the soccer socks from the living room and close the bedroom doors.

Rex: You're my type. Not a perfectionist but enjoy people.

Andrea: I know a woman who started a writers' critique group in her home while she was caring for her mother. Twice a month she filled her house with writers. Stimulating!

Kahn: Another idea is to belong to a caregivers' support group.

Rex: Speak of the devil. I thought that's what this was!

Rex: This one's not going on forever. What will we do when it is over?

Kahn: Join one or start one.

Andrea: Contact agencies to ask about support groups. They may be led by a social worker, a nurse, a chaplain, but they don't have to be. I see them listed in hospital newsletters. You may be able to attend a hospice support group even if you don't have a loved one in hospice.

Scott: I'd like one for teens, not that you guys aren't nice. You are really nice.

Lucia: My teenagers would love to meet you. Let's arrange it.

Scott: Great.

Andrea: There is more support than we realized. The world's best kept secret—support groups for caregivers.

Kahn: Not a secret now. We have blown their cover.

Andrea: I am amazed about how kind people are. I didn't know I had so many friends until Granny became ill.

MRS. GOLDSTEIN: I tried to be the super-hero caregiver. I thought I was showing love. But, my great love didn't show very much when I got tired and cranky. Now, when friends offer, I'm going to say, "Yes," then think up a task for them. I might be surprised at how many tasks can be delegated and how supportive people could be. Getting practical, what are some tasks that can be delegated?

ANDREA: Almost anything. Laundry, picking up prescriptions, grocery shopping, or vacuuming . . . Vacuuming. I want to permanently delegate that task. There is also raking leaves, weeding, taking the car in for a tune-up, having the tires rotated, picking up postage stamps, or mailing a package. The neighbor and I made a deal: If I listen to her daughter read every day, she will run errands for me on her way home from work. It works out for both of us.

MRS. GOLDSTEIN: The neighbor takes my garbage out to the street for me. It may seem like a small thing, yet the garbage is one more task to add to the others. I, in turn, make him cherry blintzes. His cherry tree is over-productive. That's the give-and-take of friendship. While we are talking about friendship, we could talk about senior citizen centers. We do so many things that people will want fake senior ID. I'm waiting for you to tell me that I look too young.

KAHN: I'll say that you are young in spirit.

Lucia: Our school has community education. Classes vary from dried flower arranging to computer classes, from photography to financial investing, from kids' gymnastics to senior citizen ballroom dancing, from golfing to writing classes. I've made some friends. What are you interested in, Scott?

Scott: I hang out with the Jet-Ski crowd when I'm home. Lucia's teens could come with me some weekend. They'll get the hang of it. It's a skateboard with a motor for the water.

 Write

MRS. GOLDSTEIN: I love opening the mailbox and finding a letter among the bills. A little card, a short note—even if I can't make out the handwriting—brightens my day.

REX: Like Kahn said. If you send 'em, you get 'em.

MRS. GOLDSTEIN: I know that. If I was organized . . .

LUCIA: I tried a Zip-Lock freezer bag. The quart size. It keeps stamps, envelopes, pens, stationary, and address book together, which can be carried to office visits, the boys' sports events, or to the bedroom if my husband is asleep. Postcards or note cards have less room to write, so I don't have to write very much. Then it is their turn to write.

REX: Right. If it takes becoming a pen pal, a man's got to work to get what he needs. Every man needs a horse, a dog, and letters.

KAHN: I have a system for Christmas cards. I know it is summer, but I have sent Christmas letters late, just renamed them New Year greetings, Valentine greetings, or Happy Easter. Late Christmas letters never held up the holidays from actually happening. I typed the addresses on the computer and printed them on adhesive-backed sheets. The first year, I didn't have a printer that could handle those sheets, so the print shop copied it for me. Since then, I bought the kind of sheets that my jet printer can use. If you want to get a little cheer in the mail, you have to send some cheer out first. Oh, well, whatever it takes.

ANDREA: There are all kinds of paper, every design that one would want. Letters are ways to be a friend even if you don't have much money or time. I learned this from working full-time. Some of the things I have sent in a note were decorative shoelaces, tea bags, stickers, book-marks, collector stamps, handkerchiefs, pressed flowers, photos, baseball cards, makeup samples, maps, sachet, spice samples, children's drawings, recipes, poems, cartoons, quotes, newspaper clippings, flower seeds, cassettes, key rings, fortune from a fortune cookie, or crafted stamped notepaper. That's me—a postage stamp friend, a thirty-two-cent friend.

☂ Celebrate Your Faith

Mrs. Goldstein: Such a variety of people! I have watched children learn to walk, bud into teenagers, work toward college, go off to college, wait for love, fall in love, fall out of love, meet their love, marry, wait for children, have children, and then I watch their children continue the cycle. I appreciate the long-term relationships. Participating within the embrace of our faith! What I covet—sorry about that sinful word—is their time. Some have more time than I do.

Kahn: You're right. That variety of ages and interests and skills seems to be the key to how the church people help each other. They offer whatever they have, whether it is time or money or expertise. The church in our neighborhood arranged rides for my wife when she had daily chemo, which I really appreciated, because I didn't have to miss as much work. Their coordinator called me for the dates and I didn't have to make any calls.

Lucia: Here's my deal: I'll trade a batch of cookies for an extra two hours of sleep. Seriously, I've received food, too. My friends from my parish brought over food every night for several weeks when my husband was in rehab. What a relief to not have to worry about how to feed a house full of teens. I ate better, too. I appreciated disposable containers because I didn't have to return them.

REX: The youth in our ward helped with yard work and grocery shopping. A group of men put shingles on my roof where it was leaking. How could I ever thank them for that?

ANDREA: Thank God; they are his people. No one mentioned prayer. We have a prayer chain for immediate prayer requests. The leader calls whoever is on his list. To me prayer is not my magic wish list, rather it is friends of my faith holding me up for God's blessings. Priceless! If you have a health problem, it makes sense to go to the creator. One woman told me after her surgery that she was going to heaven piece by piece. Another lady was given a goodbye party before her surgery. I said, "How awful!" She told me the rest of the story: It was a "Goodbye to a body part party" and helped her a lot to have the support of her friends. She called it unique and humorous. Have I grossed you out yet?

SCOTT: No, I'm not grossed out. Grandpops doesn't have a church. He doesn't get out much. I take him to the doctor and that's it.

ANDREA: Our church visits the sick. Ask him if he wants a visit.

SCOTT: Is that ok?

ANDREA: Of course. That's what faith is about, caring for people.

MRS. GOLDSTEIN: There is nothing else that fortifies like faith acted out in the . . . routines of people's lives . . . for decades . . . for centuries . . . forever.

REX: Shall we get the dictionary? I think of fortified milk, fortified with vitamin D. Strengthened? Enriched? Enhanced? Uplifted?

ANDREA: Anything that sounds supporting is good for me. If it gives me strength, I'll take it. What are some of those things?

MRS. GOLDSTEIN: That's a hard question. If someone encourages me and doesn't find fault, that gives me strength. A compliment. A pat on the back. The little things like a phone call, a card, a visit. I would take a kind word in any form.

ANDREA: Here's my story: My friend came by on her usual visit to pick up groceries for us. But, this week, she brought by a nursery catalog. I've been daydreaming of masses of bulbs, and now I can daydream about next spring *and* flowers. With my green thumb, the bulbs will probably be only a dream. I hope that bulbs are foolproof.

REX: Yes, they're foolproof.

MRS. GOLDSTEIN: I'm trying to accept strength from others. And give strength to others. One person builds up another. It's mutual. It is an attitude.

REX: It helps me keep going.

MRS. GOLDSTEIN: A little encouragement goes a long way! Oh, the marvels of teamwork—a result of God's love within us.

Embrace Your *Emotions*

 Forgive

MRS. GOLDSTEIN: Forgive? Are we supposed to dive right into this? Shouldn't we work up to it gradually? Before I can forgive, I want to know the rest of the story. I want to explore the reasons, make sure they are good ones, check out that I will be forgiven, too, and make sure I'm not too easy on people . . . and . . . make sure it is the right time, and that I'm ready. Yet, I understand that forgiveness is my own attitude rather than how much the other person deserves to be forgiven.

KAHN: You are honest, so I can admit it. That's where I am, too. To even think about forgiveness opens up the door to a scene that I don't want to look at. Two of my wife's sisters became invisible when my wife started chemo, leaving the other sister to be the helper. If bitterness were resolved, the air would be cleared . . . for us rather than for them. Forgiveness would be a way to start over.

MRS. GOLDSTEIN: Letting go.

KAHN: Part of me says, "Not in this case."

LUCIA: It's worth exploring, because forgiveness stops the rehashing. And if I wasn't rehashing it over and over, we would be able to get on to something fresh and . . . vibrant is the word.

KAHN: Hash. Meat leftovers cut into small pieces and fried with potatoes and onions. But rehash . . . would that be adding more leftovers to the old leftovers? Yuck!

LUCIA: Descriptive! Forgiveness is to throw away the old stuff and make new memories.

KAHN: Got it, at least in theory.

LUCIA: Right on! I'm thankful that I didn't have to tell a specific story.

KAHN: Hard work, but refreshing. Can you help me with this?

LUCIA: It seems that we can talk about the principles, but no one can do it for you. People are different, and there are times that an illness (and the whole package it comes with) is overwhelming. We work it through in different ways and different times, and sometimes not at all. No one can tell you how to give the other sisters the space to deal with their own grief, even though they are paralyzed when you need them most. Now, is that statement philosophical enough?

KAHN: I'll think about it. What's your situation?

LUCIA: I already said I'm full of philosophy, but not ready to talk about forgiving the one I'm thinking about. See, you are ahead of me.

Cry, Hug, Laugh, Giggle

LUCIA: Cry. Is that what we do if forgiveness doesn't work?

ANDREA: Sometimes you crack me up.

LUCIA: How terrible of me, trying to be funny when we are talking about crying. I know some serious things about tears; they contain chemicals that act like morphine. Dulls pain. Makes one euphoric.

ANDREA: I'll take some of that.

LUCIA: Once you get it going, you might as well give yourself a big dose. It's messy, makes the face wet, looks terrible if you look in the mirror. But it works!

ANDREA: I do feel better after a good cry. It's like releasing the pressure under a volcano. I think more clearly and am ready to tackle life again.

MRS. GOLDSTEIN: Being older than you, I've had more experience. When my soul is ready to break, I sob until my chest feels like it will explode. Then I am wiped out. After the crying is over, I'm ready for a fresh start.

ANDREA: Tears bring hope? Amazing. The body chemically manufactures hope when we need it most. That's a simplistic way to explain it, but it is true. Why aren't the men talking?'

KAHN: Don't have anything to say.

LUCIA: It's not macho, huh?

KAHN: Mmm.

LUCIA: All the things the women said are true. You should *unmacho* yourself and try it.

KAHN: Not right now. But I'll remember what you said.

MRS. GOLDSTEIN: While we discuss crying and laughing, why don't we bring up hugging? I know God loves me, but I want to feel human arms. That's what I think a hug is. God's touch. Oh, the power that helps every problem!

KAHN: Hugs don't cost any money and don't require experience, but practice doesn't hurt.

REX: I like my little grandchild's arms wrapped around my neck, or, when The Missus lifts her one strong hand up and strokes my face, I lean in for a hug.

MRS. GOLDSTEIN: That is so touching. I feel like I intruded on a special moment.

REX: She is special.

MRS. GOLDSTEIN: One of my most comforting times was also my saddest. Our whole family was sobbing, and we fell into one big spontaneous hug. We didn't know who was who in the tight, slippery wet mass of elbows, and necks and shoulders and arms . . .

SCOTT: That makes me think of the times I had no words to say, but Coach quietly gave me a hug—an arm over the shoulder one.

KAHN: Athletes have those moments! Let's continue with the happy topics.

LUCIA: I noticed that the men are talking now. Laughter has the same benefits of crying, but it's lots more fun. My experience with laughter is lots like Mrs. Goldstein experience with crying. There is a pause until I catch the funny side of the situation. My muscles keel me over, my throat spasms until I chortle. After that, I'm completely relaxed, yet alert. Even my memory is better.

KAHN: Laughing lightens us up. I love to come home from work and hear the kids laughing. The youngest ones are gigglers. Giggles are laughter gone overboard. It makes the day look brighter. Their musical laughs go up the scale like crystal chimes on a summer evening.

LUCIA: You're so poetic. I think you're allowed to laugh at night, too. I've been told that laughter is beneficial to the circulation, respiration, digestion, and brain. It is good for anxiety, depression, and helps us to cope. Somehow, laughter rebalances me.

MRS. GOLDSTEIN: That's my kind of thing. Start shyly. Let it creep up on you until you gasp for breath and snort through your nose. And for the quieter type, remember that giggles feel good even if they look ridiculous.

REX: Watch for the funny side of life. Real life can be funnier than comedy. Some true stories are hilarious, which is why I love to tell stories.

ANDREA: My husband teases me when I boil the teapot dry. He asks if I am running a vapor experiment, then tells me that I am depleting my supplies.

MRS. GOLDSTEIN: The senior citizens danced the soft-shoe to the tune of Swanee. We sang our own words, "Oat bran, oat bran. How I love ya, how I love ya, my dear ol' oat bran." Got it? It was the first time the soft-shoe was done with our own canes.

KAHN: Humor writers see the funny side of life. I'll make a list of humor writers for the end of our discussions. A good guffaw is better than medicine.

 Give Thanks -

LUCIA: This should be up there with forgive, because it is hard to do. Like forgiveness, thankfulness is an attitude that doesn't come naturally. What is there to appreciate? How do we recognize what is good? I'll try to think of some ways. Maybe when things look hopeless, we could start a list of what we are thankful for. Keep adding to it. Even if our house is noisy and active and always full, those noisy people love me.

SCOTT: I'm thankful for Grandpops. I hope he lives a long time.

REX: I remember the good times The Missus and I had.

LUCIA: I think of the things that I take for granted, like food. We are blessed with food, and seldom think about it. I keep three kinds of hot peppers. My kids down *fajitas* so fast that the kitchen crew at the Hyatt in Austin, Texas, couldn't keep up. I could be thankful that they have healthy appetites and are healthy. My cupboard is filled with canned goods. Not ordinary foods, but what those who go hungry would consider gourmet food: avocados, olives, sour cream, and many kinds of cheeses.

REX: I get discouraged that I can't keep up with household repairs, which I could change to appreciating that it is paid for.

LUCIA: What is honest, just, pure, lovely, good, think on these things. That's from Philippians 4:8.

SCOTT: What is that again? Think about things that are honest, just, pure, lovely, good.

REX: Back to thankfulness. When I plant seed, I anticipate a productive crop. That helps me focus everything toward harvest. I *see* the harvest when I buy the seed. I oversee the quality of seed, fertilizer, water, weed control, and the harvest. I put the right conditions together—except the weather that I'm not in charge of—and the rest is a miracle.

SCOTT: I'm thankful for criss-crossing the lake and Jet-Ski rooster tails and the thrill of stepping across a mountain creek.

ANDREA: Is there chocolate on the other side?

SCOTT: No, there's a Big Mac on the other side.

REX: I am thankful for the fine things in life: a fish on my line, making my limit, and the creek running in spring. Since The Missus and I slowed down, we appreciate different things than we did when we were younger. I am thankful for my family. The wee ones are so sweet, and they give me a lease on life, knowing our family is represented throughout eternity. We don't need money, or fame, or prestige—as if we ever achieved it, anyway. We value a good name and a reputation for being honest.

ANDREA: I expected life to quiet down when I took off from work. I expected to have more time for my children, and my garden, and to have time to get to know my mother better. My professional job was replaced with running her to the doctor, picking up medicines, trying out foods that she might eat, worrying about her blood pressure, and the swelling in her legs. . . . What am I supposed to be thankful for? I haven't found it yet.

MRS. GOLDSTEIN: Take your time; ease into it gradually. I'm thankful for life. With Papa ill, we are looking at the edge, and we are beginning to accept it, but life is a gift, not to be taken for granted. Papa says that his body is like a Rolls Royce, and he isn't going to treat it like a Volkswagen wrecker.

KAHN: My wife and I have lots of discussions. Chemotherapy has changed everything in our lives. I feel like a dragon broke into our house. Part of me is thankful for chemo, for it gives us hope for a cure. I am not thankful for it everyday, though. My wife and I are closer together, more in love, and more committed. I, like Mrs. Goldstein, have a more acute sense of the gift of life.

MRS. GOLDSTEIN: I believe in taking one day at a time. Today, this hour, this minute is sometimes all that I can handle. If I make it through the night, then through the day . . .

LUCIA: It isn't easy to accept this time of my life. I wish I could learn that. I need my energy for my responsibilities. I need to release my care, put them in God's basket, and let him carry the basket for me. This is not easy, especially at mealtime. It is frenzied. Oh, well, my family knows that when the smoke detector goes off, dinner is ready.

Embrace
Your *Spirit*

 Breathe

REX: Breathe? I expected to talk about some new ideas, not something that I've done for seventy-odd years—since the doctor slapped my bare behind.

MRS. GOLDSTEIN: Breathing is about life. The miraculous, awesome gift of breath is the gift of life. I think it is a good discussion. Caregiving is about life. We respect the life of our loved ones and want them to have as much out of life as they can. That's why we are caregivers.

REX: Even a car uses air—for combustion.

MRS. GOLDSTEIN: Oh . . . deep breathing is invigorating. It puts a generous supply of air into your body and gives energy. Fresh outdoor air, like this mountain air, is even better. I could share what I learned in the hospital waiting room. No wonder my muscles were tight and I was exhausted . . . from sitting all day. I caught myself holding my breath, so I paid attention to how I breathed. I learned that a bolus of air refreshes.

REX: How about a demonstration?

MRS. GOLDSTEIN: My voice teacher taught me to stand like there was a cord pulling me up from the middle of my chest. Like a songbird perched on a branch, ready to sing! Breathe deep from the diaphragm. Take a slow, deep breath in for the count of eight, hold it for eight seconds, then let the air out slowly. A long sigh helps, as if warming up for singing. Do you know what? While taking care of Papa, he started humming. It is more than invigorating; it is also a stress buster for me and for Papa.

ANDREA: It works for me, too. I was taught at a management seminar to blow out my stale thoughts and breathe in my fresh thoughts. It opens up the air passages. While I'm waiting for Granny to get into the chair, I sing or whistle, to remind me to breathe more relaxed. It doesn't make Granny move faster, but it does help me to relax.

MRS. GOLDSTEIN: Relaxed breathing is also good for insomnia. I breathe in slowly as I try to relax each muscle group. Catnaps tide me over. Even if I don't get to sleep, I get rested.

REX: You're saying that breath is important. Fresh air invigorates us and helps us relax, so that we won't be out-of-breath caregivers!

 Read, Write

ANDREA: I follow Mom's habits. I read the Bible. There are a lot of discouraged people in there.

SCOTT: So you like to read about that?

ANDREA: Not particularly. I like to know there are others out there.

SCOTT: Like who?

ANDREA: Jonah, David, Solomon, Isaiah . . . and lots more.

MRS. GOLDSTEIN: I read, too, but I read up-beat stuff.

ANDREA: That's encouraging. Who do you read about?

MRS. GOLDSTEIN: Jonah, David, Solomon, Isaiah . . . and lots more.

ANDREA: Those are the same people.

MRS. GOLDSTEIN: Just different times in their lives.

ANDREA: That's why I read the Bible. It takes me from one to the other.

SCOTT: Like yin and yang?

ANDREA: You're stretching the picture. What do the rest of you read?

SCOTT: I read Stephen King . . . all of his books.

LUCIA: Give me a romance novel any day. A fire in the fireplace and a fuzzy blanket.

Scott: Any day, huh?

Lucia: Ok, on summer days, I sit on the patio by the fountain.

Mrs. Goldstein: I like comedy, so I checked out *A Marriage Made in Heaven or Too Tired for an Affair* by Erma Bombeck. Here is one of her quotes: "I didn't want my mother to be eighty-something. What it was really about was I was looking at the only buffer between me and my own mortality." Now that hits right on, humor with a serious edge to it. I read from Psalms every day. When I get all the way through, I start over. It is fresh every time. I copy a few and put them on the refrigerator door. Proverbs are witty, so I copy some of them down, too.

Andrea: I like to write down my thoughts and also quotes as I come across them. Now that my father-in-law is in the family room, I made a niche in the kitchen for a desk. I compose poems, not perfectly metered sonnets, but expressions of my heart. *The Upper Room*, *Guidepost*, and *The Secret Place* are some of the devotional books that I enjoy. *The Home Altar* is for parents and children.

Lucia: I take notes as I read in order to review later. I keep my notes for years. I write down my prayers, then when they are answered I look them up and see the circumstances around why I had asked for it.

Mrs. Goldstein: Are you saying all of your prayers are answered?

Lucia: No, but it is satisfying to write down the promises in the Bible. During one of my really, really discouraging times, I read, "I will give you back the years the locust took." I wrote it down in my journal. This is embarrassing to tell. I shook my notebook at God, and screamed, "I want to believe you, but this is an impossible promise." I told God, "You are all I've got. I am going to call your bluff. See. Here is your promise, written right here." I dated the entry and decided that I would hold God to his word and let him embarrass himself. What happened was . . . later when the issue was resolved, I had the date and time to go back to.

MRS. GOLDSTEIN: So you recommend shaking your fist at God?

SCOTT: She didn't say she shook her fist. She shook her notebook.

MRS. GOLDSTEIN: Do you recommend shaking your notebook at God?

LUCIA: No, I recommend journaling.

MRS. GOLDSTEIN: What do you write on?

LUCIA: I use a stenographer's notebook. It fits inside my purse or inside a book. I clip a pen through the spiral coil. They are cheap, so I can write as much as I want.

MRS. GOLDSTEIN: What if someone got a hold of your journal?

LUCIA: No problem. They couldn't read my writing.

 Pray

LUCIA: Sometimes I get so tired, I would like to go out and buy a bucket of sleep. I wake up in the night, lie awake borrowing problems, problems that probably won't come, problems that I should give to God.

ANDREA: I try to calm down gradually. I take a walk after supper, listen to soft music, read by a flickering candle.

KAHN: You do not.

ANDREA: How do you know?

KAHN: Because life doesn't get that idealistic.

ANDREA: Ok, I do take the walk and try to wind my day down gradually. And when it doesn't happen how I plan, I try not to let it get to me.

KAHN: That's more believable.

MRS. GOLDSTEIN: I pray, and usually fall asleep before the "Amen." I feel like I'm under God's care as I fall asleep. If God pulls the darkness over the world and tucks it to bed, then he can tuck me in, too.

REX: You are poetic. However, you forgot the sunset creeping over the sky . . . and its tranquilizing reflection flowing across the lake.

LUCIA: Ok, it was your turn to be poetic. But I like it. What would really help me is to be able to get back to sleep. Who wants to tackle that?

REX: I don't have the solution, but I'm in the same situation.

KAHN: I'll share my experience. I try to convince myself—while I'm lying there in bed—that even though lots of things need to be solved, I have only one responsibility: that is to rest my body and put it to sleep. Morning comes so soon in the construction business.

LUCIA: So, like what was already said, if only I could buy a bucket of sleep. But sleep doesn't come that way. My teenagers are a big help with their dad, but I'm still like every other parent of teens—sleep deprived. I sneak naps in the middle of the day. I dream of catching up on my sleep. Naps supposedly tide me over, but I think they are also an escape, a time to sequester, a time for contemplation. My husband contemplates, too. He conks out during the football game. If I turn off the TV, he wakes up and tells me he was listening for the score.

MRS. GOLDSTEIN: I pull a chair up to my husband's hospital bed, lay my head beside him, and doze off.

LUCIA: He's your first love, isn't he?

MRS. GOLDSTEIN: Yes. You're going to make me cry.

LUCIA: Go ahead, it's allowed. It's a way of taking care of yourself. Naps can be a time to cry or a time to think things through. I tell God what I am feeling. He listens without blabbing to anyone, and he guides me. I think it works both ways. I can listen to him, if I quiet myself.

REX: I pray because I get answers. When I got so tired that my bones ached, I prayed for sleep and got the most restful sleep I'd had since my wife's illness. I want to teach my children to pray.

MRS. GOLDSTEIN: I prayed before my own surgery, knowing that the best person to help was the one who created me.

LUCIA: What prayer means to me is that God is listening to my heart as well as my words. It is hard to believe that I have access any time. No call waiting. Even AT&T isn't that efficient. My job is to slow down long enough to pray.

REX: The Missus is a firm believer in prayer. She says that just because God doesn't go by our timing, doesn't mean he's not paying attention. You know how David waited and pleaded for God to wake up and answer.

SCOTT: I'm listening. I'm going to wait this out. Maybe it will mean something to me later.

REX: Like anything else, prayer takes practice and faith. Prayer helps me; I don't help prayer. It's that way with my crops. I plant the seed in faith. It might grow and it might not. But it's more apt to grow if I plant the seed than if I didn't.

KAHN: To sum it up, I'd say that any practice which has been effective from foxholes to emergency rooms is worth trying in your own home.

Embrace Your

Sense of Humor

 Collect Humor

REX: Now that darkness is settling, let's gather around the barbecue pit and enjoy the warmth of a fire. The next topic is humor. That should warm us up.

LUCIA: You jest, Rex. You have a great sense of humor, but I will start with a story: I laughed myself silly over my kitten. She crawled into a paper sack, then shook around, with her tail hanging out the top. She tried to turn around, but the sack was too lightweight, so it twirled with her. I watch her play with yarn, hide under the sofa. Her antics are hilarious.

SCOTT: I haven't heard anything about a dog. Most everyone has a dog. Mine is a kick. He came here with me for the summer. He likes it at Grandpops, loves the outdoors . . . and he loves the creek too much . . . comes in a mess . . . a wet mess . . . a shaky wet mess. Mom says he takes after his master. Guess why he is named Peppers?

REX: He is black and white peppered?

SCOTT: No, he tried to eat peppers when he was a puppy. He knocked a bottle of *jalapeños* off the counter and tried to lap it up. One lick and he went in to a tailspin, and we changed his name from Rex—sorry, Rex—to Peppers.

REX: That's ok. I think it's funny. Anyway, now that his name changed, I don't have to change mine.

MRS. GOLDSTEIN: Pets. Their antics catch us off guard and give us a chuckle. Our cockatoo gets jealous when friends come to the house to see Papa. The silly bird cackles to get attention first.

REX: Pets are good listeners. Their purrs, barks, or coos, or moos, or chirps have a unique way of cheering us up. Comics are a source of humor. My grandchildren left a Garfield cartoon book at our house. I think Garfield is as crazy as Lucia's kitten. I collect comics from the newspaper, except I need a bigger refrigerator.

SCOTT: You could thin them out.

REX: I think about it. But they get funnier while they hang there. Actually, one magnet can hold several cartoons. I'm running out of magnets as well as refrigerator space.

SCOTT: Hey, that's a good gift idea: buy you some refrigerator magnets.

REX: No, I'm holding out for a new refrigerator. Although no one has too many refrigerator magnets, what they do have don't match!

The assortment of magnets is almost as funny as what they hold up. What you keep on the front of your refrigerator reveals lots about you.

SCOTT: Jokes are another humor idea. Who has a joke?

REX: I do. Charlie, a crusty cowboy, was determined to get back on his horse after he was bucked off. "Of course, I can get back on Ebony. I'm lots healthier than my paperwork."

KAHN: My kids, the age they are, are in to knock-knock jokes. I am done hearing knock-knock jokes.

LUCIA: My quote is, "I don't have anything against mornings, except they come at the wrong time of day." Any other good quotes?

MRS. GOLDSTEIN: "I will lift mine eyes unto the hills, from whence cometh my help."

LUCIA: Which Psalm?

MRS. GOLDSTEIN: You caught me. Let me think. Psalm 121?

LUCIA: "Humor is to life what shock absorbers are to automobiles" is a Stan Toler quote from *God Has Never Failed Me but He's Sure Scared Me to Death a Few Times*. The *Readers Digest* is packed with quotes. Every issue.

ANDREA: Granny has a quote on her dresser. "Count my life in friends, not years." It's an old quote, which I don't know where it came from. And the one I like: "Jewelry isn't fattening!"

MRS. GOLDSTEIN: Did you hear this one? "She had so many candles on her cake, that by the time the last candle was lit, the first ones had burned out." Here's another one. "Do I look thirty-five? No, but you probably did when you were." Or "I'm thirty-five. Some of us have had more experience at it than others."

LUCIA: This one was in a parish nursing newsletter. The author was unknown. "It takes about ten years to get used to how old you are."

REX: Mark Twain can keep us laughing. Let me think of one of his . . . "If in doubt, tell the truth." Will Rogers does mostly political comments, but here's one that is not political: "Everything's funny when it happens to somebody else."

ANDREA: When our children's doctor went back to school, our second-grader asked, "What grade would a doctor start at? Would they have a second-grade for doctors?"

LUCIA: "A good laugh is sunshine in a house." I remember the quote, but not who said it. Let me think . . . Thackeray, whoever he is, from *Sketches: Love, Marriage*. Here's another quote: "The heart, like blown glass, is strong, tempered, and beautiful. It can dream the impossible, love the unlovely, and hope against the odds." Let's make a list of humor resources at the end of our session.

 Play

SCOTT: Grandpops whittles. He's good at it, too.

REX: What does he whittle?

SCOTT: Whistles.

REX: He whittles whistles? That's a tongue tangler.

SCOTT: Aah. You're teasing me. He carefully chooses a willow branch and uses his Swiss knife. I watch him and so does Pepper.

REX: Did the dog learn to whittle?

SCOTT: You're teasing again. Grandpops cuts the stick about two inches long, straight on one end and slanted on the other. He carves out the inside to make it like a pipe, then cuts a slit in the slanted end.

REX: Does it make a nice sound?

SCOTT: Some of them do and some don't. He makes them whistle better than I can. He has whittled other things too. He made chains in the wood, by leaving part of each section to make the next link. I didn't figure out how he did that. I got out my knife and I found a willow stick, and I tried it for myself. It's a good diversion.

REX: I notice that you still have all of your fingers.

Scott: Sure. A little more practice, and I'll get the knack. I mean, I'll get a whistle.

Rex: You make it sound like fun. The unique sensation of shaving wood into curly slices! It would be worth a try. The Missus used to keep a quilting frame out. Times have changed on our farm. Now, I keep a jigsaw puzzle out for her same bunch of friends—counting all the children and grandkids—the house is full of people.

Lucia: Our house is full of fun. Personally, I like music best. I play a few instruments, but I won't be performing. The banjo is my favorite.

Scott: You probably could guess what my biggest passion is . . . I skateboard.

Mrs. Goldstein: Skateboard? Heavens no! Not on your life!

Scott: It is safer than you think. I don't do 360-degree culverts. I do eighteen-inch curbs. I do quieter things, too. I play cards with Grandpops in the evenings.

Mrs. Goldstein: Mercy. I'm relieved.

 # Be Spontaneous

ANDREA: I have an example. My youngest, who can barely walk, fell in a pile of leaves. I ran to help her up, except the childishness in me won. I jumped in, too.

MRS. GOLDSTEIN: Good for you. Oh, to be young again, or at least childish. The more rigid my routine gets, the more I would like to be spontaneous.

REX: "Life is too important to talk seriously about it," from old Oscar Wilde readings. Nonseriously, my life revolves around the seasons. I would like to run off to California where it's always warm.

ANDREA: What about a weekend flight?

REX: Are you serious? Whoops, you said nonserious.

ANDREA: What would you need to arrange?

REX: Someone to care for my wife. And . . . I could ask our daughters . . . You know, it might work. It just might work.

KAHN: It's not the right time for me to travel, although I picked a handful of petunias as I came in from work.

LUCIA: I would like a leisurely bath. No phone, no mail, no chores. In our house, I'd like to be first on the list for hot water. And while I'm on this . . . I would like some shampoo left for me, a Jacuzzi and a moment alone. I can imagine bubbles, my fluffiest towels, and a good book. Mmm, the smell of bath gel. Mmm, the sound of bubbles popping. Mmm, the feel of warmness.

KUHN: I have another example of spontaneity. My youngest child plays in his sandbox. He makes mountains, pours water on them, calls it a flood, then drives his cars through it. Of course, he's barefoot, squiggling his toes in the sand. I do that with construction equipment.

REX: That's what farming is about, close to nature, close to God, and far from the checkbook. I can't get to the beach very often. The hardest part of getting sand between your toes is finding the sand.

ANDREA: Have you seen the sandboxes for executives? A marble lined box, with miniature gold-colored—maybe gold-plated—rakes and shovels.

KUHN: Now, I've heard of everything. I can see it. While talking on the phone, they rake little paths in the sand. A little swirl here, and little mountain there. Stir it up; knock it down. Beats doodling on phone books.

ANDREA: Whether it is cool and wet . . . or dry and warm, it is sensuous and playful. When the going gets rough, it will be, "Take me to your sandbox."

I have a story. One morning I was hurrying off to work. A thorny branch was bent across the sidewalk by the front porch. I stepped around so I wouldn't get stuck. At eye level—I kid you not—was a perfectly shaped rosebud. With morning dew! I should have stopped to smell the rose. I should have picked it. For when I got to work, there was a person there who had just been told that her daughter died. There was my rosebud, left unpicked at home. I wish I'd have listened to my inner voice.

REX: Don't feel bad. We understand. I have another idea for spontaneity. Our house needed a lift-me-up. I draped a fishnet on the wall and pinned up the get-well cards.

KUHN: Whew! A smelly idea!

REX: A fishnet from a party store, not from a boat!

LUCIA: My teens buy me an Ansel Adams calendar every year. I collect them. You don't have to be able to afford his photos. He's dead now, so they must be expensive.

ANDREA: I like the Thomas Kinkade calendars. His pictures *are* of homey homes. Hang them on the wall and that is your homey home. A different one for each month! I buy his postcards because they can be put in little frames, or sent as postcards. The people who I sent them to told me that they saved them.

LUCIA: I could use some new toss pillows . . . Maybe recover the ones I have. [Sigh] The ones I have are true to their name—tossed.

REX: My sister bought me and The Missus new kitchen curtains. Red checked. I thought she was wacky, but she hung them for me. You know, it did brighten up the kitchen. It wasn't such a crazy idea.

KAHN: I think my wife would like new kitchen towels. And potholders. How do potholders get so dirty?

ANDREA: It's too complicated to explain.

Embrace
Your *Hopes*

Embrace Your Hopes

ANDREA: There is something profound about watching plants grow. I keep it simple: I have an Amaryllis bulb that came in its own pot. Water it and, whoopti-do, a beautiful flower. I go for the red. But I'm thinking of getting an apple-blossom colored one next time. The bulbs can be saved from year to year, but they won't bloom for me again.

KAHN: Maybe it's not their fault.

ANDREA: Be nice.

KAHN: I have a cactus. I forget to water it, and it survives. It is a Christmas cactus and blooms again at Easter.

ANDREA: It can't be; it is either a Thanksgiving cactus, a Christmas cactus, or an Easter cactus.

KAHN: Do you know that? Maybe mine is a multiholiday cactus.

ANDREA: Maybe it is disoriented.

KAHN: I say live and let live. Let it bloom any time it wants. What's the farmer got to say?

REX: I don't grow cactus, or cacti. I grow sugar beets. All of it is work. It is the kind of work I like to do, in spite of every challenge Mother

Nature sends me. From the time my sugar beets emerge from the soil until they are harvested, I am in awe. When you see a hundred acres of miracles, you can believe in other miracles.

KAHN: Hey, that's what my cactus is. A miracle!

LUCIA: The miracle I see is the power in the waves. I go to the beach and watch the waves. They pound away, all day . . . forever. All that power amazes me . . . The moon pulls the entire ocean and makes the tide change. It is so much bigger than I am. [Sigh] Inspiring.

SCOTT: Wow. I go to the beach and think that the sand is older than Grandpops.

ANDREA: I watch the sunset. We live on a hill that looks over the lake. The sunset stretches out . . . like pours . . . across the sky. But that's not all. It stretches across the lake, too. The movie—or I could call it a panorama—keeps playing until dark. And the next night, a new movie comes on. That gives me hope—there will always be a new movie tomorrow.

REX: I watch my grandkids. Their little muscles learn new tricks. Their little brains learn new things. Life goes on. That gives me hope.

MRS. GOLDSTEIN: For you it is sunsets, for me . . . it's the things that can't be taken away. The past, the memories. I remember when my husband and I met. We were teenagers playing volleyball outside our synagogue. His hair bounced when he spiked. The muscles in his arms cascaded when he served. I was young and in love; he took my breath away. When I help him turn in bed, I have those memories. There is hope in retaining my heritage. What I learned from my parents, I passed on to my children. We cling to the traditions which held our people together for centuries. This gives me hope.

SCOTT: This group has helped me appreciate what is going on now. Grandpops and me. He can't see very well, but he sees more about life than I do. I guess my mom taught me this, but I do enjoy this summer with Grandpops. He tells me about Normandy—I hadn't known he was there in the service. He plays a mean harmonica. I could learn from that. It is as if I am in a time warp this summer. The good thing about being here this summer is that it gives me hope for what is ahead in my life.

LUCIA: My hope is in the future. Maybe my husband will fully recover. Our teens are learning responsibility that will help them be good adults. I hope that someday I will get enough rest.

KAHN: I'm going to miss this lodge. Maybe I'll stay here overnight. How do we say goodbye? I am going to miss you after we leave. What if we each share an idea to close?

LUCIA: I hope you feel as if you have been embraced.

ANDREA: May you be uplifted during this unique time in your life. Remember to take care of yourself.

Mrs. Goldstein: May this be a reflective time to value the memories that you share with your loved ones.

Rex: May you be convinced that you are precious, too.

Lucia: May you survive the experience, enjoy the adventure, and even deepen your relationships. And most important, get your rest.

Scott: Kids are caregivers, too. And I have something else to say. I hope you have a Grandpops as good as mine.

Kahn: Are we going to get together again?

Lucia: I hope so. I'd like to discuss chronic pain or chronic disease.

Mrs. Goldstein: Or aging.

Andrea: How about weight loss?

Rex: Or how to listen.

Kahn: How to live with grief.

Scott: Or more for teens.

Lucia: Count on me. I'll be back.

Appendix

Ideas of what friends and family can do

Acts of friendliness to counteract loneliness and appeal to the senses:

- Telephone. Ask if this is a good time to call.
- Make an appointment to visit.
- Send a singing telegram.
- Relieve caregivers so that they can attend a wedding or graduation.
- Write a note or letter. Don't wait until you have special paper.
- Set up e-mail on computer.
- Start a round-robin letter, cassette, or video within the family.
- Offer to videotape the family photos.
- Offer to pick up a rental video or buy upbeat videos.
- Buy or lend them a video camera and film.
- Invite a caregiver to a coffee klatch.
- Purchase scented sachets, bath salts, oils, or bubble bath.
- Arrange a trip to the library for books, audiocassettes, or videos.
- Order a *National Geographic* membership by calling 800-NGS-LINE.
- Order *Smithsonian* magazine by writing: *Smithsonian* magazine, 900 Jefferson Dr., Washington, DC 20560.

- Send seasonal, unbreakable, small, disposable decorations such as banners, balloons, windsocks, or posters.
- Offer to sit while caregivers take a nap.
- Relieve them so that they can get a haircut, keep dentist appointments, attend a fitness class, play bridge, or get to their temple, synagogue, mosque, parish, church, or ward.
- Relieve them so that they can browse through a craft store, music store, nursery, fabric store, hardware store, or auto supply.
- Buy plenty of colorful paper plates, napkins, or cups. Buy lots of colorful towels and sheets.
- Volunteer to take clothes to dry cleaners, take film in for developing, do grocery shopping, pick up medical equipment or prescriptions, take their car to the shop, rotate their car tires, organize transportation assistance, or haul soil, fertilizer, or mulch for their garden.
- Decorate pillowcases with lace and ribbons and edging. Buy extra pillows of all sizes.
- Paint or post their house number in a visible place. Install bright lights in the entry.
- Donate money or time for housecleaning service or yard maintenance.
- Buy them a ticket to a concert, movie, or play.
- Buy them a prepaid phone card.
- Choose a gift or inspirational book.

GIFTS OF FOOD TO COUNTERACT PHYSICAL FATIGUE AND PROVIDE NOURISHMENT:

- Home-cooked meals in disposable containers
- Ice cream with toppings
- Blocks of cheese
- Packages of deli meat
- Baked potatoes with toppings
- Tea bags and a teacup
- Fruit with peeler and a china fruit dish
- Flavored vinegars
- Small coffeepot
- Decorative thermos
- Crazily-designed sports bottle
- Nuts in a wooden bowl
- Dried fruits in glass candy dishes
- Gift certificate from a restaurant
- Ingredients for ethnic foods:
  - Irish soda bread mix, jar of jam
  - pasta, sauce, garlic bread spread, dried pasta
  - pizza mix, canned Canadian bacon, olives, and cheese
  - Matzo ball mix, chicken broth
  - canned tamale sauce, flour tortillas
  - cheddar cheese soup

- Send mail-order food gift packages such as those from:
    - Harry and David Food and Plant Gifts, 800-547-3033
    - Aldercove Custom Seafoods, 800-321-FISH

ENCOURAGEMENT COUNTERACTS GRIEF AND OFFERS HOPE

ENCOURAGE THE SPIRIT:
- Arrange for someone to be available by telephone.
- Give "Making Memories Scrapbook" supplies.
- Give or lend an inspirational book, cassette, or poster.
- Organize a prayer chain for their requests.
- Ask if they would like clergy to visit.
- Give or lend the Bible on tape.
- Remember them in prayer.
- Give a blank book for journaling.
- Arrange for them to receive magazines such as:
    - *The Upper Room*, 615-340-7252; *Guidepost*, 212-251-8100
    - *The Secret Place*, 610-768-2240; *The Home Altar,* 612-330-3423

ENCOURAGE WITH SYMBOLS OF LIFE:
- Deliver plants such as amaryllis, bonsai or ficus or ivy.
- Give a pet such as a bird, cat, dog, or fish. Be sure to ask.
- Preserve memories of family with scrapbooks.

- Purchase an art or inspirational calendar.
- Order Jackson and Perkins Roses nursery catalog, 800-854-6200.

ENCOURAGE WITH CREATIVE OPPORTUNITIES

ART:
- Organize artistic supplies for crocheting, knitting, needlepoint, quilting or counted cross-stitch. Furnish supplies for ceramics to paint, clay for modeling, sculpture media, stained glass, carving tools for wood, origami, oil, acrylics, watercolors, or pastels.
- Thomas Kinkade paintings, Lightpost Publishing, 800-366-3733
- *Christianity and the Arts* magazine of religious art, 312-642-8606
- *Eretz: The Geographic Magazine from Israel*, 800-681-7727
- Scrapbook supplies: Design Originals, 800-877-7820. Optic Graphics, Inc., 410-768-3000. Artistic Albums & More, 888-9ALBUMS
- Klutz Publishing activity books from knots to magnets

MUSIC:
- Braun Journey harp and instrumental music, 503-228-5113
- Sonya Kay "Sunday Blues" CDs and Cassettes, 425-787-2552
- Gaither Homecoming Videos, videos, cassettes, CDs, 800-955-8746
- Music stores may have interesting folk musical instruments

HUMOR:
- Car Talk on National Public Radio, Saturday morning
- Fellowship of Merry Christians catalog, humor books, 800-877-2757
- *Readers Digest* subscription, newsstands, Pleasantville, N.Y. 10570
- Bob Basso, *555 Ways to Put More Fun in Your Life*, 800-243-0495

PROFESSIONAL ASSISTANCE:
- Case Management Society of America, 501-225-2229
- Children of Aging Parents, support groups, 800-227-7294
- Eldercare Locator Service, 800-577-1116
- National Assoc. of Area Agencies on Aging, 202-296-8130
- National Assoc. of Home Care, resource catalog, 202-547-7424
- National Assoc. of Professional Geriatric Care Managers, 520-881-8808
- National Family Caregivers Association, 800-896-3650
- National Hospice Organization, literature, referrals, 800-658-8898
- U.S. Administration on Aging, 202-619-0724

PUBLICATIONS:
- *Caregivers Handbook*, item #04-3, by Jim and Joan Boulden, 800-238-8433
- *The Sandwich Generation* magazine, 732-536-6215

Questions for Group Discussions

WELCOME

In this setting, each person shares as they are comfortable. Each person who wishes to share can introduce themselves. Share about your family. These questions are to help you get acquainted:

- Which character do you identify with?
- What is your main reason for being here?
- What brings you to the caregiving role?
- How long have you been a caregiver?
- What was like you expected? What was different?
- What is the most pressing issue that you are now facing?
- What do you expect from this group?

EMBRACE YOUR BODY

Chapter One: Sing
As you can see, this is a light-hearted, humorous group.
- What could help your spirit soar, so that you could sing?
- If you soul could sing, what songs would you sing?
- What does music do to the soul?
- What ways can we bring music into our homes?
- Discuss setting up a music exchange or lending library, such as CD or cassettes or videos—or maybe instruments or sheet music.

Chapter Two: Energize
Each of us searches for more energy. It's universal.
- What are some causes of fatigue?
- What are some ways you have tried to renew your energy? What has been successful?
- If you had the opportunity, what would you try?
- What is the relationship between emotional vitality, spiritual vitality, and physical strength?
- What exercise works best for you?
- What are the precautions for exercise?
- What is a reasonable exercise goal for you? Why? When?

Chapter Three: Eat

There are several food plans that provide balanced nutrition.

- What food plan to you use?
- Discuss the various food plans such as the Food Pyramid, Weight Watchers, American Heart Association, American Diabetes Association, or vegetarian food.
- What ethnic foods do you like?
- What role does the scale play in your life?
- How does the food you eat coordinate with the food you prepare for other people?
- If you were going to make any changes in your food, what would it be? Why? When?
- How could you make eating more fun?

EMBRACE YOUR FAMILY

Chapter Four: Love

Love is an emotional word, but it is also a practical verb.

- What ideas do you have about sprinkling the air with love?
- What is the relationship between love by voice and love by action? Can one influence the other?
- How did you meet your loved one? What attracted you to them? Them to you?
- What are some romantic ways to show love?

- Why would delegating care show love?
- Do you have some ideas of what to try this week?

Chapter Five: Remember

Stories bring out the child in us as well as preserve family heritages.

- Do you remember stories that you heard as a child?
- Have you recorded any of your stories?
- What place fosters story-telling? Campfires? Around the table? Riding in the car?
- What is it about stories that bring out the child in us?
- Why do we like stories?
- Do you have a story to share?

Chapter Six: Communicate

Our ability to communicate through language both written and spoken is a valuable human characteristic.

- What are the principles of listening?
- Why is listening important compared to talking?
- Why are some things difficult to express?
- What is the importance of confidentiality?
- What helps us to trust someone?
- How do you maximize communication?
- Do you have an urgent message for your loved one?

Chapter Seven: Pop Popcorn

Popcorn offers crunch, nutrition, popping, and friendship.

- What is the nutritive value of popcorn?
- What entertainment ideas would you like to share?
- What would help you be more comfortable in having friends over?
- What ideas interested you?
- What would you need to start a support group?
- What are some ways your friends could help you?

Chapter Eight: Write

Communication keeps us connected with our friends and family.

- How do you keeping in touch with friends and family?
- Can you delegate letter writing?
- What supplies would help you?
- What are some ideas of mailable gifts?
- Do you have a memorable experience of receiving something in the mail?
- Do you have special pens, paper, envelopes, or address labels?

Chapter Nine: Celebrate With Your Friends of Faith

Your friends of your faith offer support.

- What have you experienced with friends of your faith?
- What practical ways could your friends help you?
- Is there a system to minister to caregivers? Tell them your needs.
- Would you like to share a story about prayer in your life?

EMBRACE YOUR EMOTIONS

Chapter Ten: Forgive

It is very difficult for us to forgive, yet it miraculously changes our lives.

- How is forgiveness related to caregiving?
- What keeps us from forgiving?
- Do you have a story about forgiveness?
- What is the first step in forgiveness?

Chapter Eleven: Cry, Hug, Laugh, Giggle

Emotions can be expressed in an active, outward way.

- Do you feel that you have permission to laugh?
- Why is it okay to cry?
- Do you have a "hug" story?
- What gives you the giggles?

Chapter Twelve: Give Thanks

Giving thanks is an action, being thankful is an attitude. Neither is easy.

- Why do we resist giving thanks?
- What are some of the things that we are thankful for?
- What is in it for me, to give thanks?
- Do you have a story about someone telling you thanks?
- Why are people slow about giving thanks?
- Are there issues in your life that make it hard to be thankful?
- Do you have a quote about giving thanks?

EMBRACE YOUR SPIRIT

Chapter Thirteen: Breathe

Something as natural as breathing, can be a tool for relaxing.

- What relaxation technique works for you?
- What deep breathing exercise relaxes you?
- How do you know when you are tensed?
- How is whistling, singing, and humming related?
- What is the importance of relaxation and caregiving?
- What could others do for you?

Chapter Fourteen: Read, Write

Learning from others, and expressing yourself revives the spirit.

- Do you journal? How? When?
- How do you find the time to journal?
- What do you like to read?
- Do you like talking books?
- What kind of reading do you do?
- What is the value of reading? Journaling?
- Do you have some tips for others?

Chapter Fifteen: Pray

Most everyone believes in prayer.

- Do you have a testimony about the effects of prayer?
- How do you find the time to pray?
- What are some principles of prayer?
- What are some ideas to help us pray?
- Do you know a mighty prayer warrior? Do you wish you did?
- How do you teach your children to pray?
- What is the use of praying?
- Do you have a quote about prayer?

Chapter Sixteen: Collect Humor

Humor resets us, helps us view ourselves and the situation in a different light.

- What kind of humor do you like?
- Who is the funniest person you know?
- Why do we like humor?
- What does humor do for us?
- Do you have a story, joke , or quote to share?
- How do we find humor around us?
- How do we bring humor into our homes?
- What humorous thing could you do right now?

Chapter Seventeen: Play

Playing is not just for kids.

- What is the value of play?
- What playful things do you do?
- How do we get into a playful mood?
- What was the funniest thing that you've done?
- Who are do you associate with that brings out the kid in you?
- Where do you feel the most playful?
- What hobby or recreation would you like to learn?
- What do you do now, that you enjoy?

Chapter Eighteen: Be Spontaneous

Oh the thrill, to jump into something quickly!

- What gives you permission to be spontaneous?
- Who do you know who is spontaneous?
- What are the risks? The benefits?
- What adventure do you dream of?
- What risk would you like to take?
- Do you have a wacky story to tell?
- Do you have a "playing in the sand" story?

EMBRACE YOUR HOPES

It is profoundly encouraging to look ahead, to dream, and to hope.

- What encouraging word do you have to share?
- What encourages you?
- Do you have a sunset story? A beach story? Another story of hope?
- Who is the most encouraging person that you know?
- Was *Hugs for Caregivers* helpful to you?
- What topics would you like to discuss in the future?
- What have you learned from caregiving?

About the Author

As a home-visiting registered nurse case manager, Pauline Sheehan empowered homebound clients and their families to cope. As Director of Nursing Service (DNS) with a nursing home administrator's license, she counseled caregivers as they made decisions about assisted-living arrangements. As cardiac rehab instructor, she guided families toward a zest for life. As a certified diabetes educator, she mobilized diabetics to live a robust life. As a professional writer, she publishes fiction, articles, humor, health, and drama, and speaks on these topics.

She relied on her husband as her caregiver during a four-year illness, and she faced caregiving issues with her children, sister, and father.

She enjoys her grandchildren, children, her harp, and her shade garden. Pauline also praises God for her husband.

Her B.S. degree in health-care administration and thirty years in the health-care profession developed her specialized skills, experience, and empathy to write *Hugs for Caregivers*.

About the Artist

Charlotte Terhune's appreciation of the human heart permeates her watercolors. Her studio is a haven where concepts are transformed into visual expressions that evoke a sense of happiness.

Hugs for Caregivers
$9.95 plus $3.95 shipping and handling.
Washington residents pay 8.2% sales tax.
For credit card orders call 1-800-917-BOOK.

Checks may be sent to:
Hugs for Caregivers
G 701, Suite 155
303–91st Ave. NE
Everett, WA 98205-1599

Inquire about workshops and speaking
engagements.